Welcome to my Fabulous Things to Make and Do book!

Inside you'll find simple step-by-step instructions for lots of craft projects, to bring some colour and style to your bedroom, create some fun accessories or make a beautiful gift for a friend or family member. Some projects are more difficult than others: one bow means the project is easy, two means it is medium, three means it is more difficult and you may need an adult to help you.

Younger Hello Kitty fans will need to ask an adult to help them with cutting, gluing and sewing, and always ask an adult before using any materials or photos for a project. You will need a large, well-lit surface to work on. Remember to cover it with a cloth or sheet to protect it before you begin. You will also need an apron to protect your clothes. Don't forget to clean and tidy up once you have finished!

So what are you waiting for? Let's get creative!

Love,

Hello Kitty

x

First published in the UK by HarperCollins Children's Books in 2011

© 1976, 2011 SANRIO CO., LTD.
ISBN: 978-0-00-789778-0

A CIP catalogue record for this title is available from the British Library.

Printed and bound in China

Hello Kitty bookmark

Every bookworm needs a stylish bookmark to make reading even more fun!

Difficulty rating: easy!

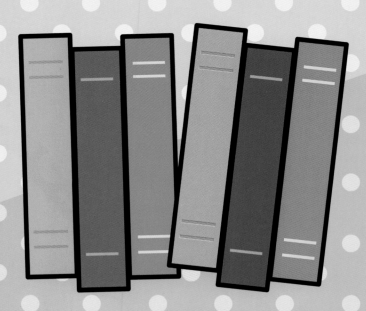

You will need:
a piece of thin card, A4 size
a black felt tip pen
a red felt tip pen
a yellow felt tip pen
a pencil
a ruler
scissors
a glue stick/PVA glue
decorations (glitter, sequins etc)
other coloured felt tip pens
black wool

How to make:

1 Using your pencil and ruler, draw three sides of a rectangle onto your card, approximately 6cm wide and 16cm high, leaving room at the top of the paper for my head.

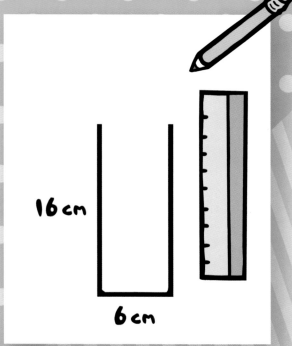

16 cm

6 cm

2 On top of your rectangle, draw the outline of my head. Don't forget, my bow will stick out of the top and side. Then draw in my eyes, nose and bow in black pen, and fill the bow in using red pen. Fill my nose in using a yellow pen.

3 Cut round your outline carefully, then cut six small pieces of wool for my whiskers and stick them onto my face.

PVA

4 Now you can decorate the bookmark however you like. I love gluing glitter and sequins onto my bookmarks in circular and star patterns. Or you can colour it in using your brightest colours – it's up to you! Don't forget to decorate both sides.

Door hanger

Handy for letting people know when they can come to visit you in your bedroom, and when you want some peace and quiet!

Difficulty rating: easy!

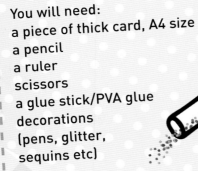

You will need:
a piece of thick card, A4 size
a pencil
a ruler
scissors
a glue stick/PVA glue
decorations
(pens, glitter,
sequins etc)

How to make:

1 Using your pencil and ruler, draw three sides of a rectangle, approximately 9cm wide and 12cm high.

2 On top of your rectangle, draw a hook, as shown in the picture here. This will need to be the right size to hook over your door handle.

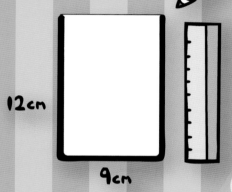

12cm

9cm

3 Cut round your outline carefully.

4 Now it's time to decorate your door hanger. On one side of your door hanger you will need a 'Welcome' or 'Come in' message, on the other you will need a 'Do not disturb' message. You can personalise the messages to say whatever you like!

HELLO KITTY'S ROOM COME IN!

HELLO KITTY'S ROOM DO NOT DISTURB!

Hello Kitty mask

Great if you want to go to a fancy dress party dressed as me!

Difficulty rating: easy!

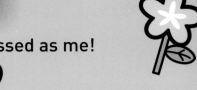

You will need:
a piece of tracing paper
a piece of thin card, A4 size
a pencil
a black felt tip pen

a red felt tip pen OR
red material (e.g. felt, but it's up to you!)
black pipe cleaners
PVA glue
scissors
thin elastic (approximately 35cm long)

How to make:

1 Trace the mask outline on the opposite page using a pencil and your tracing paper, then cut it out and place it on your card. Draw round it carefully.

2 Next, draw in the outline of my bow in black pen. Then colour it in red, or stick your red material onto it.

3 Cut out your outline, hold it up to your face and mark with a pen where you will need the eye holes to go. Poke through these holes and cut round them neatly until they are big enough for you to see through. Then, cut six pieces of pipe cleaner (approximately 4cm long) and stick three on each side of your mask using PVA glue.

4 Make two small holes with your scissors, one on each side, just above the whiskers. Thread the elastic through one hole and tie a knot in the end so it doesn't pop back out.

5 Place the mask over your face, pull the elastic tight round the back of your head, then thread the other end through the other hole and knot it in place.

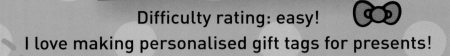

Gift tags

Difficulty rating: easy!
I love making personalised gift tags for presents!

You will need:
tracing paper
thin card (pick a light colour that you can write on)
a pencil
a ruler
a glue stick

scissors
any of the following:
coloured pens
ribbon
glitter
sequins

any other details you would like to add. There are so many things you can try!

How to make:

1   First you need to decide on a shape for your tag. Here are some templates you might like to use. Trace them using tracing paper, then cut your tracings out and draw round them on your card.

2 Now you can start thinking about the design you would like to use to decorate it (this will depend on what paper or bag you are using for the gift). Here are some ideas for things you could use to decorate your tags: glitter, sequins, coloured pens, paint, old jigsaw pieces, dried flowers, felt shapes, ribbon, stickers, buttons, tissue paper, pictures from magazines. There are no rules, so it's up to you! Here are some examples:

GLITTER

SEQUINS

TISSUE PAPER

FELT

SEQUINS

3 Write your message on the back of your tag. Finally, make a small hole somewhere near the top of your tag, thread a piece of ribbon through it, and tie or stick it to your wrapped present.

Happy Birthday!
Love
Hello Kitty
x

Pop-up cards

Difficulty rating: easy!

Pop-up cards are so much fun, and easy to make too!
So next time you need a card for a friend or family member,
give one of these simple pop-ups a go.

You will need:
two pieces of thin card, A4 size
scissors
a glue stick/PVA glue
a pencil
pens
glitter, sequins etc

How to make:

1   Fold a piece of card in half, shorter sides together.

2 Take one piece of card and find the centre of the short side, then make two cuts about 4cm long, 4cm apart from each other on either side of the central point, to create your flap.

3 Fold the cut section back to create a crease. Now open your card and pull the flap inwards towards you.

HAPPY BIRTHDAY!

4 Now you can stick whatever you'd like to pop up onto the flap. Simply design it on your second piece of thin card, cut it out and stick it to your flap (measure it to make sure it won't stick out of the card when it's folded closed). Then you can decorate the rest of the card however you like!

Door sign

Difficulty rating: easy!

A cute door sign is a great way to identify which room is yours!

You will need:
a photo of yourself
coloured card (whatever
size you'd like your sign
to be)
ribbons
a glue stick/PVA glue
pens
glitter
sequins
scissors
a pencil
a ruler
sticky tape
or adhesive putty

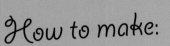

How to make:

1. Decide on a shape for your sign and draw it onto the card, then cut it out.

2 Stick the photo of yourself in the middle, and decorate around it. You could cut the photo into a shape too, e.g. a circle.

3 You might want to add a message to say, for example, 'Sarah's room, keep out', or you might prefer just to have a picture. It's up to you!

4 Add as many decorations as you like to your sign.

5 Fix it to your door at eye level using sticky tape or adhesive putty, but check with an adult first.

Paper lanterns

Difficulty rating: easy!

Paper lanterns are a simple way to brighten up any room!

You will need:
sheets of A4 paper,
various colours
scissors
PVA glue

How to make:

1 Take your first piece of paper and fold it in half, longer sides together. With the fold at the bottom, cut slits upwards approximately every two centimetres, but leave a few centimetres' gap at the top.

2 Unfold your paper, and put a line of glue down one of the shorter sides. Curl the paper round and glue this side to the other short side to form your lantern.

3 To make the handle, cut a strip of paper from another sheet of A4 and glue the ends to the top of the lantern. You can make as many as you like, and hang them on string across your room!

Phone/MP3 cozy

Difficulty rating: medium

Cozies are a great way to protect your phone or MP3 player,
and making your own means you can design it exactly to your taste!

You will need:
felt or fluffy material
a pencil
scissors
a needle and thread
a button
decorations
PVA glue

How to make:

1 Take your piece of felt and fold it in half,
then lie it on your table. Take your phone/
MP3 player and lie it on top of your felt.
Draw round your phone leaving a little space
on each side. (You want your cozy to fit as snugly
as possible, without being too tight.)

2 Cut round your pencil line so you are left with two separate pieces of material. Sew them together at the bottom and up both sides, leaving the top open so you can slip your phone/MP3 player in. Turn the cozy inside out to hide the knots at the end of your stitches.

3 To keep your phone/MP3 player secure, you will need to add a flap and button. Cut another piece of felt for this, and make it as thick as possible (3 or 4cm wide is good).

4 Sew it securely to the back of the cozy, near the top. Pull it over the top of the cozy and cut a hole in it the right size for your button. Finally, sew your button securely in the right place on the front of your cozy, pop your phone/MP3 player in, button it up and you're all done!

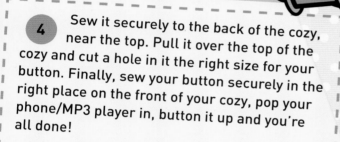

HELLO KITTY

5 If you would like to add any more decorations to your cozy, you can! You might want to stitch some more felt shapes on, or glue on some decorations such as glitter or sequins, or write your name on it in colourful glitter glue.

Picture frame

Difficulty rating: medium

I love photos, but frames can be expensive to buy. Why not make your own frame from the things you have in your home?

You will need:
a photo or picture
thick card
a pencil
a ruler
scissors
a glue stick or PVA glue
decorations
a magnet or string/ribbon

How to make:

1 Find a photo or picture you would like to make a frame for. Lie it face-down on a piece of thick card and draw round it with a pencil.

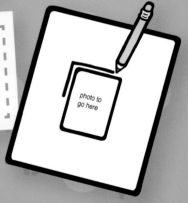

photo to go here

2 Add 5cm to each side of the rectangle/square you are left with, and draw another larger one around it. This will be the outside of the frame.

3 Minus 1cm from each side of the original rectangle and draw a third, smaller one. This will be the inside edge of the frame which will keep your picture in place.

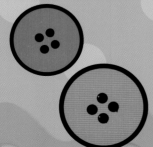

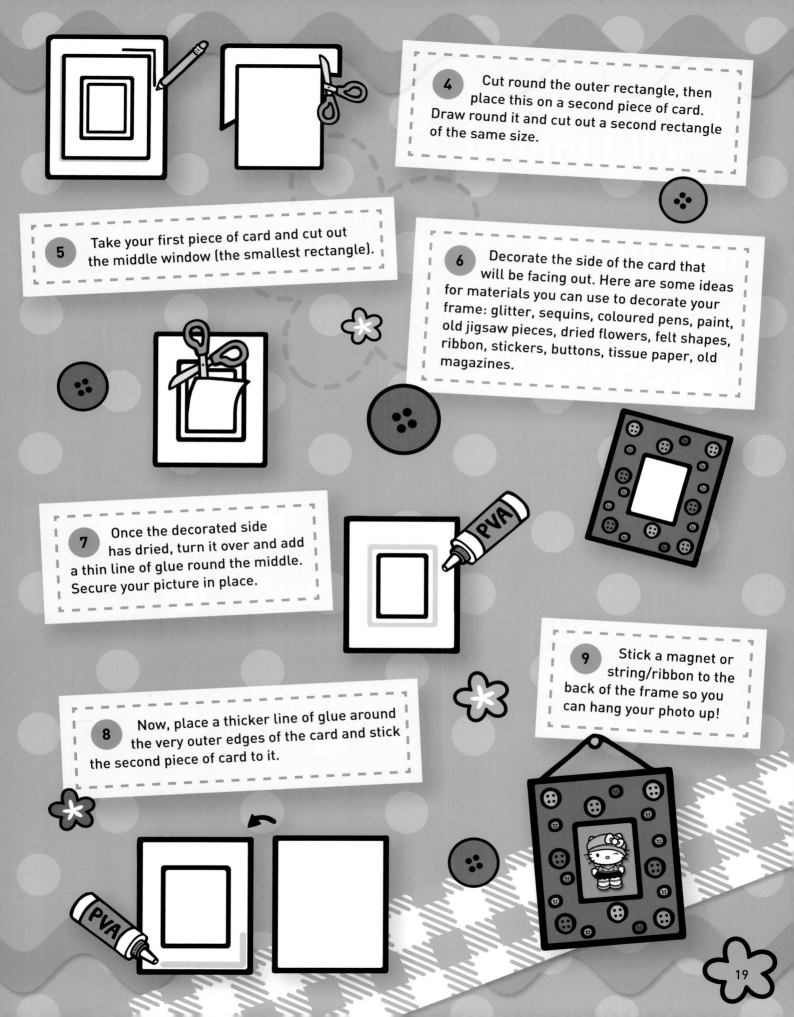

4 Cut round the outer rectangle, then place this on a second piece of card. Draw round it and cut out a second rectangle of the same size.

5 Take your first piece of card and cut out the middle window (the smallest rectangle).

6 Decorate the side of the card that will be facing out. Here are some ideas for materials you can use to decorate your frame: glitter, sequins, coloured pens, paint, old jigsaw pieces, dried flowers, felt shapes, ribbon, stickers, buttons, tissue paper, old magazines.

7 Once the decorated side has dried, turn it over and add a thin line of glue round the middle. Secure your picture in place.

8 Now, place a thicker line of glue around the very outer edges of the card and stick the second piece of card to it.

9 Stick a magnet or string/ribbon to the back of the frame so you can hang your photo up!

Tissue paper flowers

Difficulty rating: medium

A beautiful bouquet of tissue paper flowers makes a wonderful present, and can brighten up your bedroom all year round!

You will need:
tissue paper in various colours
green pipe cleaners
scissors
sticky tape
a vase or a ribbon

How to make:

1. Cut out lots of circles from your tissue paper, using as many colours of paper as you like. The circles can be any size. You can either draw round a circular object like a mug, cut wavy edges (so they look like clouds), or you might want to use pinking shears for a really spiky finish.

2. Stack as many circles as you would like to use for one flower on top of each other, in whatever colour combination you like. Next, take a green pipe cleaner and push it through the middle of your tissue paper circles. If there are too many circles for the pipe cleaner to push through, you can add each circle separately.

3. Once the pipe cleaner is all the way through, fold the end back over on itself to hold the tissue paper circles in place, so that it looks like a small hook.

4. Scrunch up the paper and arrange the tissue paper to look like petals. If your tissue paper circles are slipping down the pipe cleaner, you can secure them in place at the base with sticky tape.

5. You can make as many flowers as you like, using different colour combinations and sizes of circle. When you've made enough, arrange them in a vase, or tie them together with a pretty ribbon!

21

Hello Kitty bow Alice band

Difficulty rating: medium

Now you can wear your very own Hello Kitty bow in your hair!

You will need:
a thick black Alice band (padded or material, not plastic)
red felt
tracing paper
PVA glue
a black pen
scissors
a needle and thread

How to make:

1. Using this bow as a template, trace round each section separately on your tracing paper, then cut them out and draw round them on your red felt. There are 4 sections altogether.

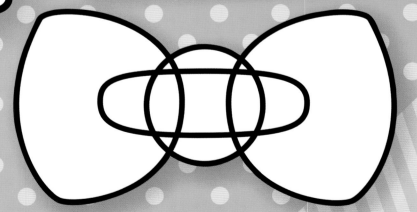

2 Cut the pieces from your felt and glue them together.

3 Once they have dried, stick or sew the whole thing to your Alice band in the position shown here.

PVA

Wall collage

Difficulty rating: medium

Do you have lots of pictures all over your room that you would like to hang together as a collage? It will make your room look much neater, and is lots of fun to make!

You will need:
a large piece of card
or a cork board
pictures
wrapping paper
tissue paper
paint and paintbrush

glitter
ribbon
decorations, depending on
what you would like to use
to make your collage
a glue stick/PVA glue
scissors

Once you're done you will need to ask an adult to hang it on your wall using a nail and hammer.

How to make:

1 Gather together all the pictures you would like to use in your collage. They might be drawings you have done, posters of your favourite band or celebrity, photos of you and your friends/family, things you have cut out of magazines, whatever you like!

2 Next, take your board and decide what background colour you would like to use. You can either paint your board in your chosen colour, or stick paper or material onto it. You might want to sprinkle glitter onto your paint as it's drying to make it look even prettier!

3 Once your board is covered in a colour, arrange your pictures/posters/photos in the pattern you would like, and stick them down.

4 Add decorations, scraps of pretty paper etc around your pictures to finish off your collage.

Padded hangers

Difficulty rating: difficult!

Fancy designing your own super-stylish padded hangers for your clothes?

You will need:
wooden hangers
wadding
a ruler
scissors
a needle and thread
masking tape
fabric
pins
ribbon

How to make:

45 cm

5 cm

1 First, choose the fabric you would like to use for your hangers. Next, cut two pieces of wadding 5cm wide and 45cm long, and place one on top of the other.

2 Push the hook of a wooden hanger through the centre of the wadding, then wind the wadding round the wooden arms of the hanger. Tape into place with masking tape. Trim the ends of the wadding and sew them closed over the hanger ends.

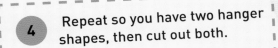

3 Place the hanger on your chosen fabric and draw round it, adding 2cm in each direction so you can sew up the seams.

4 Repeat so you have two hanger shapes, then cut out both.

5 Pin your fabric in place over the hanger (one piece on the front, one on the back). Tuck the edges of the fabric in, then stitch both pieces together carefully, so that they fit tightly around the wadding.

6 Finally, tie a piece of ribbon around the neck of the hanger hook for a pretty finish.

Bag

Difficulty rating: difficult!

You can make yourself a stylish tote bag out of an old T-shirt or jeans! Here's how:

You will need:
an old pair of jeans or a T-shirt
scissors
a needle and thread
a ruler
a black pen
a medium-size bowl
chalk
pins
decorations

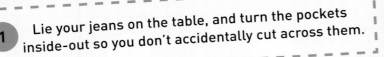
How to make: Jeans

1 Lie your jeans on the table, and turn the pockets inside-out so you don't accidentally cut across them.

2 Cut the legs of the jeans off at the crotch.

3 Neatly stitch up the holes where the legs used to be.

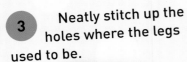

4 You can use the cut-off legs to make a handle. Cut a strip 5cm wide and 50cm long. Sew each end securely to the top of the handbag.

5 Once you're done, you can add more decorations to your bag. You might like to thread a belt through the belt holes, or add glitter, or stitch some pretty patterns on. It's up to you!

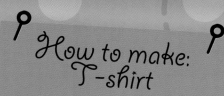

How to make: T-shirt

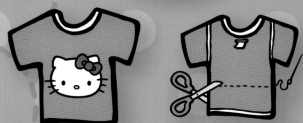

1 Find an old T-shirt that doesn't fit any more, and that has a cool design that you'd like to turn into a bag, or a plain T-shirt that you can decorate yourself!

2 Turn your T-shirt inside out and sew a line of stitches along the bottom, wherever you would like the bag to finish. Cut off the excess material and put it to one side.

3 Turn your T-shirt back the right way. Cut off the sleeves, then put them to one side with the rest.

4 Turn your T-shirt inside-out again. Place your medium-size bowl half over the neck of your T-shirt and draw round it using your chalk. This is to give you a wider opening at the top of your bag; the neckline alone will be too narrow.

5 Pin the front and back of your T-shirt together under this line, then carefully cut along the line. Pull out the pins, turn your T-shirt back the right way again and you're finished! If you used a plain T-shirt you can decorate it however you like.

Difficulty rating: difficult!

You can turn any wooden or thick cardboard box
into a beautiful personalised jewellery box!

You will need:
a wooden or cardboard box
paint
a paintbrush
a ruler
felt or velvet material
thick card
a small mirror
PVA glue
decorations
glitter glue

How to make:

1 Find a box the right size for your jewellery. Make sure it has a lid. If you don't have one lying around the house, you can buy boxes from craft shops. If you do have one lying around the house and it has drawers, even better! You can also use a shoe box, or a strong cardboard box.

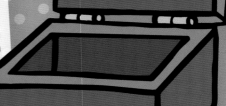

2 Give your chosen box a wipe over, then paint the outside and the entire lid in your chosen colour. Leave to dry.

3 Next, measure out how much felt you need and stick it to the bottom and inner sides of the box so that your jewellery will be protected.

4 If you would like multiple compartments for your jewellery, measure out pieces of thick card and place inside your jewellery box. You might also like to cover these in material or paint them.

PVA

5 If you would like to add a mirror, glue it carefully on the inside of the lid.

PVA

6 Time to decorate your jewellery box! You could write your name in glitter glue on the top of the lid, then add other pretty details around it, stick stickers onto it or paint designs on top of your layer of base paint.

HELLO KITTY

Hello Kitty's essential craft supplies

I'm sure this book will have given you a taste for crafts!
If you'd like to keep making things at home, here's a list of my essential
craft supplies to keep handy for when you're feeling creative:

Old sheet, or plastic table cover
Apron
Glue stick
PVA glue
Scissors
Ruler
Coloured paper, A4 size
Coloured thin card, A4 size
Thick card
Pencils
Coloured pencils
Felt tips
Pipe cleaners, various colours
Thin elastic

Wadding
Chalk
Paints
Paintbrushes, various sizes
Glitter glue
Sequins
Glitter
Needle and various colours of thread
Wool, various colours
Felt
Beads, assorted
Wire
Buttons, assorted

You can also recycle lots of household products
to use when making craft projects, but remember
to check with an adult first. Here are
some ideas to get you started:

Cereal boxes
Toilet rolls
Plastic bags
Old clothes
Shoe boxes
Foil
Egg boxes

Plastic bottles
Bottle tops
Magazines
Newspapers
Old wrapping paper
Old greetings cards
Drinking straws

Happy crafting!